To lesley
Have fun in your garden
with love
Carol x

THE COMPLETE
GARDEN
PLANNER AND RECORD BOOK

ANNE CHRISTIE

Published in 2001 by Caxton Editions
20 Bloomsbury Street
London WC1B 3JH
a member of the Caxton Publishing Group

© 2001 Caxton Publishing Group

Designed and produced for Caxton Editions
by Open Door Limited
Langham, Rutland

Written and compiled by Anne Christie
Photography: PhotoDisc

Printed in Indonesia by APP Printing

Title: The Complete Garden Planner and Record Book
ISBN: 1 84067 282 X

The Complete

GARDEN

Planner and Record Book

CAXTON EDITIONS

CONTENTS

A seasonal diary for you to use each year as your garden develops.

Containing useful information, records and planting guides for each season.

CONTENTS

Snowy, Flowy, Blowy,

Showery, Flowery, Bowery,

Hoppy, Croppy, Droppy,

Breezy, Sneezy, Freezy

The Twelve Months. George Ellis

INTRODUCTION

Good gardens do not just happen, they develop over time. Without some knowledge of the soil and the plants it

can grow, no-one can make a good job of creating a new garden.

Some new gardens begin as a bare piece of ground with nothing but builder's rubbish, soil and weeds; others may

be simply unimaginative and dull, needing a new design and planting.

Every site is different and creates different problems for the gardener who takes on the challenge and

responsibility of creating a new garden. If you have decided to create a new garden, the essential elements are

good planning and record keeping.

PLAN AND CREATE
A NEW GARDEN

All you need to grow fine strong grass, is a crack in your path.

Anon

A New Garden

There are very few places where plants will not grow. Assess your garden and try to choose plants which are attuned to the conditions provided. What your garden has to offer will provide you with a sensible basis for choosing new plants and making worthwhile improvements to your existing garden.

Your Existing Garden

A beautiful garden is a rewarding achievement.....

• *photograph your garden before you begin so that you have a record of what it looked like before you transformed it.*

SIZE: _____

SHAPE: _____

FACING DIRECTION: _____

CLIMATE: _____

SOIL TYPE: _____

EXISTING PLANTS
AND FEATURES

PERENNIALS

ANNUALS AND BIENNIALS

poppies
marigolds
lupins

BULBS

daffodils

tulips

bluebells

CLIMBERS

clematis

Russ. Ivy

honeysuckle

TREES AND SHRUBS

beech

sycamore

STRONG FEATURES

Spring colour

WEAK AREAS

top RHS (f. of large window)

top border - weeds

hse wall - weeds.

PROBLEM AREAS

Adapting an Existing Garden

AREA PLAN:
• *Use these grids to draw areas of your garden to scale.*
• *Record the exact position of existing plants and plan for future planting areas and special projects by using a numbered key for each area.*
• *Photocopy the page so that you can record the changes in your garden over the years as you incorporate new ideas and planting.*

KEY TO AREA 1

(per) 1 Saponaria Ocymodes   Ap. M
(per) 2 Centaurea Dealbata   Ap 11
3 peonie
4 azaela
5
6
7
8
9
10
11
12
13
14
15
16
17
18

19
20
21
22
23
24
25
26
27
28
29
30
31
32
33
34
35
36
37

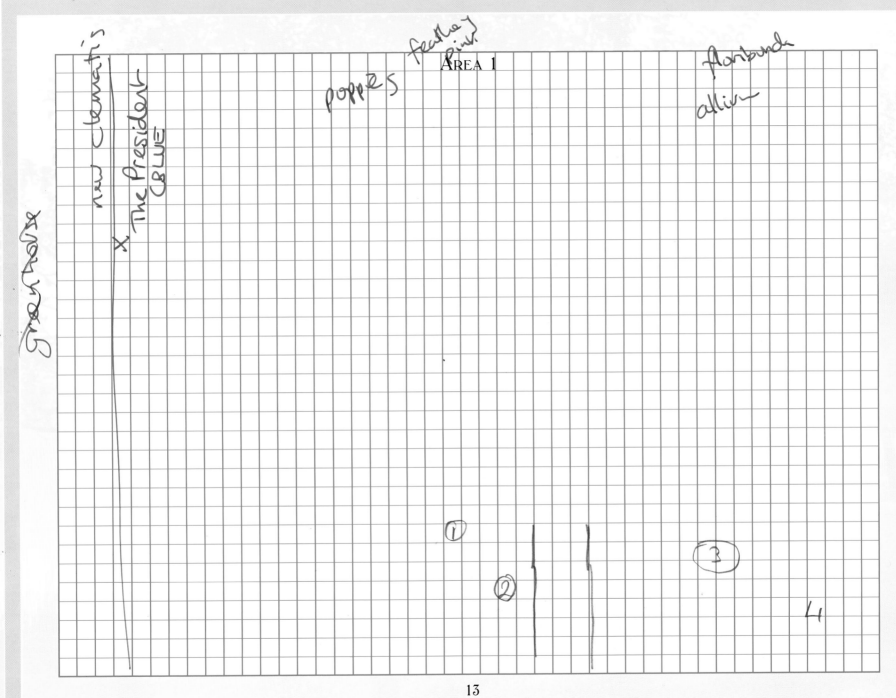

TOP

AREA 1

Greenhouse

new clematis

x The President (BLUE)

poppies

feathery pink

floribunda allium

① ② ③ 4

13

KEY TO AREA **2**

1 _____
2 _____
3 _____
4 _____
5 _____
6 _____
7 _____
8 _____
9 _____
10 _____

11 _____
12 _____
13 _____
14 _____
15 _____
16 _____
17 _____
18 _____
19 _____
20 _____

21 _____
22 _____
23 _____
24 _____
25 _____
26 _____
27 _____
28 _____
29 _____
30 _____
31 _____
32 _____
33 _____
34 _____
35 _____
36 _____
37 _____

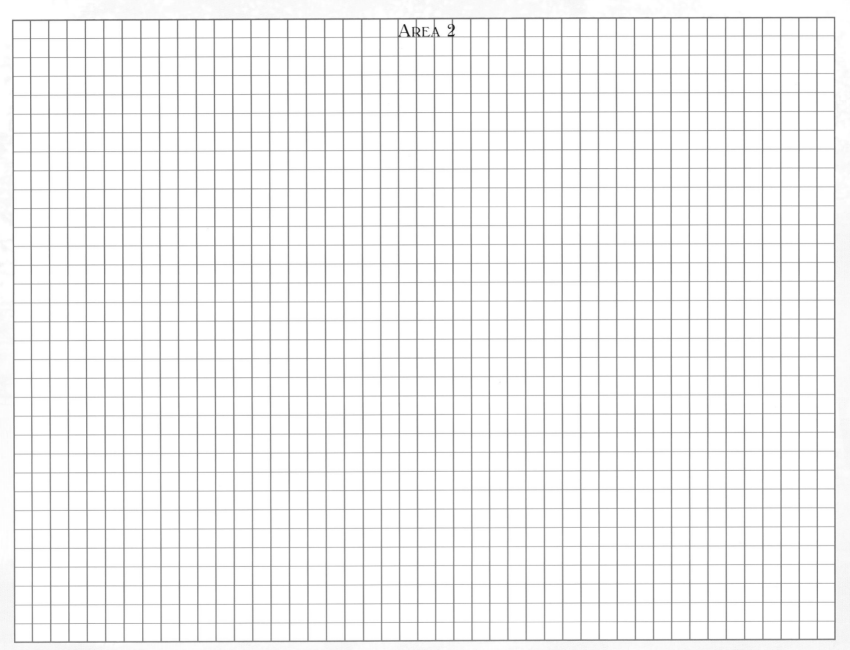

KEY TO AREA **3**

1 _____

2 _____

3 _____

4 _____

5 _____

6 _____

7 _____

8 _____

9 _____

10 _____

11 _____

12 _____

13 _____

14 _____

15 _____

16 _____

17 _____

18 _____

19 _____

20 _____

21 _____

22 _____

23 _____

24 _____

25 _____

26 _____

27 _____

28 _____

29 _____

30 _____

31 _____

32 _____

33 _____

34 _____

35 _____

36 _____

37 _____

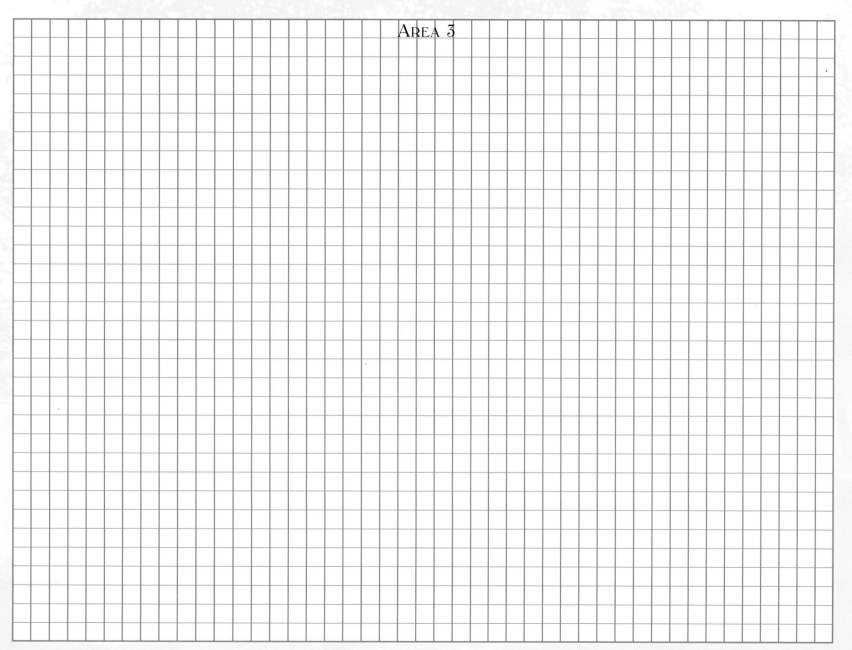

AREA 3

Costs and Budgeting

Record of Purchases and Costs: Year 1

PURCHASE	DATE	AREA OF GARDEN USED	SUPPLIER	COST
alpines	April 07	bottom patio	Threaplands	£60
ground cover (vica)				
+? +?				
tub, marigolds				
sweetpeas - trailing & climbing				
tomato p. x3				
cucumber (1)				
3 clematis			Aldi	£9
wall paint; red ivy - floribunda rose			Decora	4?
hosta,	(June)		Logie	22
			TOTAL FOR YEAR	

RECORD OF PURCHASES AND COSTS: YEAR 2

PURCHASE	DATE	AREA OF GARDEN USED	SUPPLIER	COST
			TOTAL FOR YEAR	

RECORD OF PURCHASES AND COSTS: YEAR 3

PURCHASE	DATE	AREA OF GARDEN USED	SUPPLIER	COST
			TOTAL FOR YEAR	

RECORD OF PURCHASES AND COSTS: YEAR 4

PURCHASE	DATE	AREA OF GARDEN USED	SUPPLIER	COST
			TOTAL FOR YEAR	

RECORD OF PURCHASES AND COSTS: YEAR 5

PURCHASE	DATE	AREA OF GARDEN USED	SUPPLIER	COST
			TOTAL FOR YEAR	

RECORD OF PURCHASES AND COSTS: YEAR 6

PURCHASE	DATE	AREA OF GARDEN USED	SUPPLIER	COST
			TOTAL FOR YEAR	

General Information

In any garden there are certain important points to consider when caring for and maintaining new and existing planting. These tips are reminders to read up on information which will help you create your dream garden.

TEST AND IDENTIFY SOIL TYPE

IDENTIFY WEEDS
Heavy soil
– coltsfoot, speedwell and creeping buttercup; horsetails indicate poor drainage.
Light soil
– shepherd's purse, knotgrass, pearl-wort, and spurrey.
Acid soil
– sorrel, mayweed and plantains.
Alkaline soil
– scarlet pimpernel, lamb's tongue, dwarf thistle and bladder campion.

IDENTIFY PROBLEMS
Cold, exposed site
Hot, dry site
Shade
Coastal garden
Town garden
Neglected garden
Annual weeds
Perennial weeds
Ground cover plants
Pests – birds and animals

THE GARDEN YEAR

SPRING

Spring the sweet spring, is the year's pleasant king

Then blooms each thing, then maids dance in a ring,

Cold doth not sting, the pretty birds do sing.

Nash

Early Spring

KEY TASKS

LAWNS AND HEDGES
• *Start planning dwarf hedges. Repair any lawn damage, revive growth and begin to mow.*

BEDDING PLANTS AND ANNUALS
• *Begin to plant sweet peas outside.*
• *Take fuschia cuttings, start growth and begin training as standards.*
• *Take cuttings of tender spring bedding plants.*

PERENNIALS
• *After flowering split up polyanthus.*
• *Grow perennials from seed.*
• *Plant lily of the valley.*

BULBS
• *Plant pot grown snowdrops.*

TREES, SHRUBS AND CLIMBERS
• *Prepare large shrubs to be moved.*
• *Revive heathers and hebes.*
• *Prune any shrubs with colourful stems and take cuttings to grow more.*

HERBS AND VEGETABLES
• *Plan a small vegetable plot.*
• *Plant early potatoes.*
• *Plant asparagus crowns.*
• *Fit in vegetables – even in a small garden.*

CONTAINERS
• *Grow roses in containers.*
• *Pot chrysanthemums for colour later in the year.*

MISCELLANEOUS
• *Buy or make a cold frame.*

Place a picture here of

your garden in spring

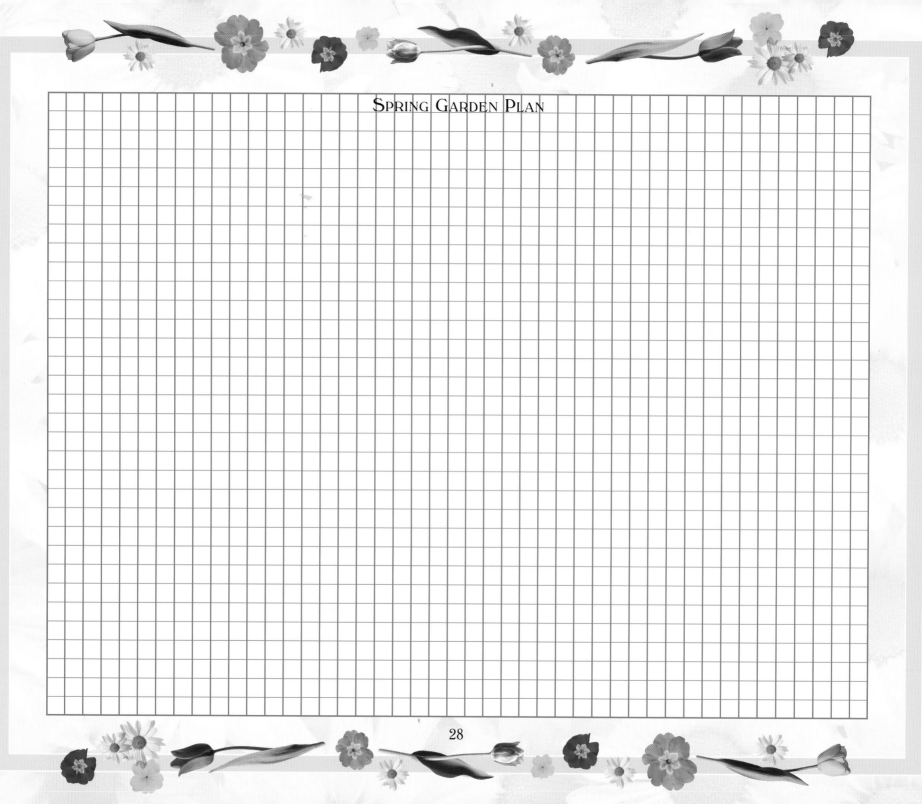

Spring Garden Plan

SPECIAL PROJECTS

FORWARD PLANNING IDEAS

TO MAKE AN ASPARAGUS BED
- *Dig deeply adding plenty of compost.*
- *Make sure drainage is adequate.*
- *Dig out shallow trenches and mound the centre to make a gentle ridge.*
- *After planting remember that there will be little to cut for a couple of seasons.*
- *The wait will be well worthwhile.*

WHEN MAKING A COLD FRAME
- *Use strong recycled timber treated with preservative.*
- *A sloping lid collects maximum light and sheds rain.*
- *Design to fit a vegetable bed with a handle at each end.*
- *Place over growing plants to protect them out of season throughout the year.*

Early Spring Task List

Work to be Done

AREA

LAWNS/HEDGES

BEDDING PLANTS

ANNUALS

PERENNIALS

TREES/SHRUBS

ROSES

CLIMBERS

HERBS/VEGETABLES

FRUIT

CONTAINERS

PATHS/PATIOS

WATER GARDENS

MISCELLANEOUS

Start now to keep your lawn in top condition.
Top tips:
- REPAIR
- REVIVE
- MOW

SOWING
Start to raise hardy perennials from seed.
- *Choose varieties of delphiniums, lupins and pinks in trays or modules.*

KEY TIPS FOR EARLY SPRING

Lily of the valley love shade. Plant now or divide and replant if they are spreading in your garden from previous years. Their sprays of scented flowers are attractive in a corner of the garden during the spring.

Snowdrops are like winter aconites – best moved and planted just after or during flowering to avoid roots drying out.

Grow early flowering chrysanthemums now to plant outside in mid spring. Make sure soil is well prepared in advance.

Many shrubs are grown for their attractive colours in winter; the bark of some brambles, dogwood and willows are especially striking. Prune them now to ensure brightly coloured new shoots. Any cut stems will root easily if large branches are pushed firmly into the soil.

Clip winter flowering heathers with shears now to ensure their shape remains compact.

Large shrubs can be successfully moved in autumn if preparation starts now. Trim the roots and encourage strong new fibrous roots to reduce the shock of repositioning later in the year.

PLANTS FOR EARLY SPRING

Parrot tulips
– provide colourful display with large heads of fringed petals - in the garden and for cutting.

Perennial double primroses
– are good highlights for containers and small beds in spring.

Flowering quince 'Knap Hill Scarlet'
– dense spreading deciduous bush – long season of bright blooms.

Evergreen shrub 'Daphne Odora'
– fragrant flowers from late winter on.

Hardy perennial Epimedium grandiflorum
– 'Rose Queen' with high clumps of tinted leaves.

Hardy evergreen periwinkle Aureovariegata
– spreads small flowers to 60cm in 2 years.

SOWING
For flowers in the late summer sow seeds thinly in moist compost.
- *Put trays on a sunny windowsill or in the greenhouse.*
- *Cover with polythene until first green shoots appear – then move into full light.*
- *Water moderately.*
- *Transfer to seed trays and move outside to cold frame.*
- *When about 5cm grow on in pots until planting in flowering position.*

PLANTS IN FLOWER AT THIS TIME

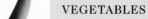

VEGETABLES

In a small garden you can grow beans, courgettes, asparagus and spinach in quantities which will happily freeze for winter use.

Place a picture of your

garden in bloom at this time.

VEGETABLES

If space in your garden is limited try growing a few vegetables in flower beds. Camouflaged by flowers they will be protected from insects and pests. Make sure they are near the border and easily accessible from the path.

VEGETABLES

Prepare beds for potatoes and plant under a sheet of black plastic.

SUCCESSFUL PLANTS

UNSUCCESSFUL PLANTS

HERBS
Herbs can make an exceptionally decorative border with their attractive flowers and leaves.

BULBS
Small beds of bright spring bulbs in any size garden can be enhanced by a frame of clipped dwarf box hedge.

Record of Purchases and Planting

NAME	TYPE OF PLANT	WHERE PURCHASED	WHERE PLANTED	DATE

NOTES, REMINDERS AND OBSERVATIONS

Fuchsias can be started now:
- *Plunge pots in water for just a few minutes.*
- *Stand plants in full light.*
- *Prune back quite hard.*
- *Cut out lifeless or spindly shoots; shorten other shoots and sideshoots.*
- *When new growth appears knock plants out of pots and remove old compost.*
- *Return to containers with fresh compost.*

SEEDLINGS
Plant out sweet peas from seedlings started in autumn or mid winter.
- *Space bamboo canes 30cm apart in a circle or rows.*
- *Fasten tops tightly to secure.*
- *Plant a sweet pea at the bottom of each cane.*
- *Hold in place with a wire ring or twist to start climbing.*
- *Continue as plants grow.*

Mid Spring

KEY TASKS

LAWNS AND HEDGES
• *Overhaul lawn mower for new season.*

BEDDING PLANTS AND ANNUALS
• *Buy summer bedding plants for growing on.*
• *Early in the season, sow annual climbing plants.*
• *Sow hardy annuals where they are to grow outside.*

PERENNIALS
• *Make a garden with scree for drought tolerant plants and alpines.*

TREES, SHRUBS AND CLIMBERS
• *When quinces stop flowering, prune them.*

BULBS
• *Plant gladioli corms.*
• *Pinch off dead bulb heads.*

ROSES
• *Feed liberally and mulch.*

HERBS AND VEGETABLES
• *Plan for late summer crops and winter supplies.*
• *Sow peas and continue at regular intervals.*
• *Sow outside main crop leeks.*
• *Sow French beans under glass in pots.*

FRUIT
• *For small gardens choose fruit trees to train into compact shapes.*

MISCELLANEOUS
• *Consider benefits of organic fertiliser.*
• *Stimulate growth of outdoor plants by feeding.*

SPECIAL PROJECTS

FORWARD PLANNING IDEAS

MID SPRING TASK LIST

WORK TO BE DONE

AREA

LAWNS/HEDGES

BEDDING PLANTS

ANNUALS

PERENNIALS

TREES/SHRUBS

ROSES

CLIMBERS

HERBS/VEGETABLES

FRUIT

CONTAINERS

PATHS/PATIOS

WATER GARDENS

MISCELLANEOUS

VEGETABLES
Grow French beans in pots.
• *They hate the cold so start them off in a warm place like the greenhouse.*

VEGETABLES
Start peas now and sow at intervals of three weeks until the beginning of summer using a first-early wrinkle-free variety.

VEGETABLES
An early variety of leek sown indoors in early spring will be nearly ready for planting out.
• *Prepare the ground now for transferring the plants in late spring.*

Key Tips for Mid Spring

Now is the time to plant annual climbers from seed.
• *Cathedral bells, nasturtiums and morning glory can be planted in a sunny spot supported by a fence or pergola.*

Save money and time by buying plugs of bedding plants from a garden centre or seed catalogue now when they are ready for transplanting.
• *Plant out when in flower in late spring after danger of frost is over.*
• *Clear up borders, cutting away dead growth, weeding and forking over soil.*
• *Remember to use compost not peat. A sprinkling of organic or rose fertiliser for new plants or those which are being moved is needed now.*

Divide sweet violets and move to a shady spot for the summer.

Now is the time to start planting herbaceous borders with summer flowering plants.

ANNUALS
Sow annuals outdoors:
• *Trickle dry sand from a bottle or thin-necked container to mark the outline of planting areas.*
• *Make parallel sowing drills with a can in each patch.*
• *Sow different seeds of varying colours and heights in each patch.*
• *Pay attention to balanced design.*
• *Weed and water until seedlings appear.*
• *When 5cm high thin seedlings to 15-20cm apart.*
• *Water with diluted feed.*

Plants for Mid Spring

Doronicums
– hardy perennials grow to 60cm for a splash of early season colour in sun or shade.

Pulsatilla vulgaris
–perennial pasque flowers in varied colours.

Clematis alpina 'Ruby'
– climbs to 10ft tall. Elegant four petalled blooms.

Prunus avium 'Plena'
– masses of drooping blooms on medium size deciduous tree.

Berberis x stenophylla
– hardy evergreen shrub with clusters of golden blooms.

HEDGES
Any shaggy or neglected formal hedges need trimming now.
• *Use a taut line to guide you for a precise finish. Clip again in late summer.*

LAWNS
A good, green, strong growing, all-purpose lawn set off by borders requires minimum labour.
• *For perfectionists a cylinder mower will give the finest cut and remove coarse grass; less frequent cutting on a general purpose lawn will do well with a rotary mower. Make sure yours also picks up cuttings.*

PLANTS IN FLOWER AT THIS TIME

ALPINES
You can make a lovely garden for drought tolerant and alpine plants.
• Add gravel to the soil to provide drainage for Mediterranean shrubs and perennials.

VEGETABLES
Throughout the season get busy sowing summer vegetables outside.
Summer cabbages, cauliflowers, carrots, lettuce, spring onions, radishes, spinach and turnips.
Plan ahead for winter!

CHOOSING ALPINES
Start with taller plants like dwarf conifers which are slow growers.
Smaller plants can include rock pinks, houseleeks, saxifrage, thrift, miniature aquilegias, dwarf hyperium and thyme.
Drought tolerant plants include rosemary and lavender.
Rock roses love sunny hillsides whilst sea-hollies, yuccas, cannas and marguerites provide summer colour.

Successful Plants

Unsuccessful Plants

GLADIOLI
*Gladioli are wonderful for cutting.
A good mixture of sizes, colours
and varieties will give a bright
splash in the garden and indoors.*

BULBS
*Daffodils are at their best in mid
spring; tulips are coming on and
many smaller bulbs are making a
wonderful spring show in the garden.*

GLADIOLI
*Plant a few every two weeks from
mid spring till early summer to
flower in succession through the
summer and autumn.*

DAFFODILS
*Pinch off the flower heads when
daffodils start to fade – this will
channel energy into building up
flowering bulbs for next year.*

41

Record of Purchases and Planting

NAME	TYPE OF PLANT	WHERE PURCHASED	WHERE PLANTED	DATE

NOTES, REMINDERS AND OBSERVATIONS

CLIMBERS
Remember to support climbers well.
• *Staple wires to fence posts or drive vine eyes or screw in eyes into mortar.*
• *Walls can provide an excellent opportunity to combine climbers like clematis and rambling roses.*

SHADE TOLERANT CLIMBERS
Camellias, clematis, flowering quince, hydrangea, climbing ivy, honeysuckle, winter jasmine, pyracantha, some roses and flowering currants all have varieties which thrive when growing on shady walls.

ROSES
Feed and mulch roses well using standard rose fertiliser and mulch of good garden compost.

43

Late Spring

KEY TASKS

LAWNS AND HEDGES
For good summer growth feed lawns well.

BEDDING PLANTS AND ANNUALS
- *Take cuttings of young dahlia shoots and plant out.*
- *Plan summer bedding and plant out.*

PERENNIALS
- *While tall herbaceous plants are small, make natural supports.*
- *For autumn flowering, plant hardy chrysanthemums.*

BULBS
- *Dig up tulips after flowering and store for next year.*
- *Build up next year's daffodils with a good feed.*

TREES, SHRUBS AND CLIMBERS
- *Make a cuttings frame for soft cuttings of garden shrubs.*

HERBS AND VEGETABLES
- *Watch out for blackfly and frosts.*
- *Plant and sow tender outdoor vegetables.*
- *Plant tomatoes under glass.*
- *Sow extra root crops to store for the winter.*

FRUIT
- *Prune cherry and plum trees.*
- *Control fruit tree growth by nicking and notching.*

CONTAINERS
Look out for vine weevils.

MISCELLANEOUS
- *For home grown fertiliser make a compost Container.*

PRUNING FRUIT TREES
In spring and summer regular pruning for cherries and plums can be done. The sap is rising and cuts will heal quickly reducing the risk of infection from fungal spores.

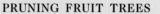

KEY TIPS FOR LATE SPRING

Towards the end of spring bedding plants need attention.
• *Begonias, alyssum, petunias and salvias can go in to fill spaces and provide bright colour.*

Don't forget that annual delphiniums and tall asters will start flowering in early-mid summer. Together with annual nemesias you will have a wonderful display of colours, pink, white, yellow, crimson and blue.

Tobacco plants, annual poppies in a range of yellows, white and orange and poor man's orchid will catch the eye.

Don't miss annual pinks and new varieties of phlox.

• *Plant out dormant dahlia tubers.*
They are tender plants which don't like even a hint of frost. Their flamboyant flowers will dazzle your garden later in the summer.

Remember when choosing dahlias that they make wonderful cut flowers.
• *Try to grow several rows of mixed types amongst the vegetables. Choose size and height carefully.*

CHRYSANTHEMUMS
For a splash of colour in the borders during the late summer and autumn, plant chrysanthemums now. Although they hate the wet, they do need continuous moisture throughout the season.
• *Make sure you dig soil well and include garden compost or good manure with a light dressing of fertiliser.*

PLANTS FOR LATE SPRING

'Molly the Witch'
– *yellow flowered peony – small herbaceous perennial.*

'Spring Green'
– *green-flowered tulip with lovely shaped blooms.*

Onondaga – viburnum sargentii
– *vigorous deciduous shrub with maple shaped leaves; grows to 3m.*

'Nora Barlow' – aquilegia vulgaris
– *hardy herbaceous perennial with double flowers.*

Allium aflatunense – 'Lucy Ball' and 'Purple Sensation'
– *ball-headed flowering onions with large round heads.*

WAYS TO SUPPORT BORDER PLANTS
Peonies form large clumps and need a stout support.
• *Set this in place before foliage develops.*

Hollyhocks, delphiniums and dahlias have tall stems.
• *These need to be secured to single stakes or canes with wire rings, string or plastic twists.*

Interlocking wire stakes can be joined together making enclosures of variable sizes to surround plants.

String and thin canes will support bushy plants. Remember not to tie the string too tight.

Cut twiggy sticks from hedges after pruning to provide the cheapest supports.

• *Attach a panel of wire netting to cane and support tall slim stems or flower stalks like border carnations.*

PLANTS IN FLOWER AT THIS TIME

DAFFODILS

When daffodils have finished flowering, give them a feed. Leave in place or store in a cool dry spot for healthy bulbs to replant in the autumn.

Plan your planting scheme to cover daffodils after flowering and hide unsightly dying leaves.

TULIPS

Dead head tulips after flowering. Dig them up and store indoors after drying the bulbs in the sun. Keep in a dry place until autumn.

CUTTINGS

Between now and mid summer you can take soft cuttings from fine bushy shrubs.

• Make a cuttings frame for propagating plants. An old wooden box with the bottom removed is ideal.

POPPIES

Welsh poppy – especially the double variety - grows happily in sun or shade.

SUCCESSFUL PLANTS

UNSUCCESSFUL PLANTS

GREENHOUSES
There will be plenty of work in the greenhouse. Tomatoes and other tender plants are most important Yellow mottling or streaks on leaves will indicate a virus – this will not wipe out the crop, but will provide a warning for next year.

COMPOST
Organic matter is the first line of defence in times of drought. Compost heaps provide food which is vital for a healthy productive garden.
• Make your own double compost bin simply from strong boards.

RECORD OF PURCHASES AND PLANTING

NAME	TYPE OF PLANT	WHERE PURCHASED	WHERE PLANTED	DATE

VEGETABLES
Cucumbers, French and runner beans and courgettes are easy to grow. There is still time to catch up if you haven't started these yet.

VEGETABLES
Winter root crops grown now like swede and salsify can either be left in the ground until needed or lifted in the autumn and stored throughout the winter.

Notes, Reminders and Observations

_____

_____

_____

_____

_____

_____

_____

_____

_____

_____

_____

_____

_____

VEGETABLES

Even in summer, frost can threaten summer crops. Cover cold frames at night, keep cloches ready and cover or earth potatoes if necessary.

VEGETABLES
Watch out for blackfly.

LAWNS

The lawn now needs feeding and will repay you handsomely if you look after it well. Liquid feeds are cheaper, fast and allow a margin for error but they can be time consuming to apply.

• Feed in both spring and summer or using a slow-release fertiliser over an extended period must be done exactly to the manufacturer's instructions.

PESTS

Vine weevil will attack begonias, cyclamen and primulas. The grubs hatch out in late spring and resist most chemicals.

• Control them with a good biological preparation which only works above 50°F so this is the time to use it. Repeat in late summer for complete pest control.

THE GARDEN YEAR

SUMMER

In winter I get up at night, and dress by yellow candle light

In summer, quite the other way, I have to go to bed by day

R. L. Stevenson

Early Summer

KEY TASKS

ANNUALS AND BIENNIALS
• *Sow all biennials including winter pansies and polyanthus.*

PERENNIALS
• *After flowering, tidy up oriental poppies.*
• *Mound violas to increase them.*
• *When hellebore seeds are ripe, sow them.*

TREES, SHRUBS AND CLIMBERS
• *After spring flowering blooms have faded, prune.*

BULBS
• *For autumn flowers, plant anemones.*

ROSES
• *Train climbing roses.*

HERBS AND VEGETABLES
• *Sow Belgian chicory.*
• *Guard against all garden pests, protect cabbages and carrots.*
• *Plant cauliflower in well prepared soil.*

FRUIT
• *Train raspberries.*
• *As shoots develop, train all soft fruit.*
• *Before fruit pests become serious, control them.*

CONTAINERS
• *Plant patio containers for the summer.*
• *For exotic displays, grow tender plants now.*

MISCELLANEOUS
• *Check all watering equipment in case of drought during the summer months.*

Place a picture here of

your garden in summer

51

SUMMER GARDEN PLAN

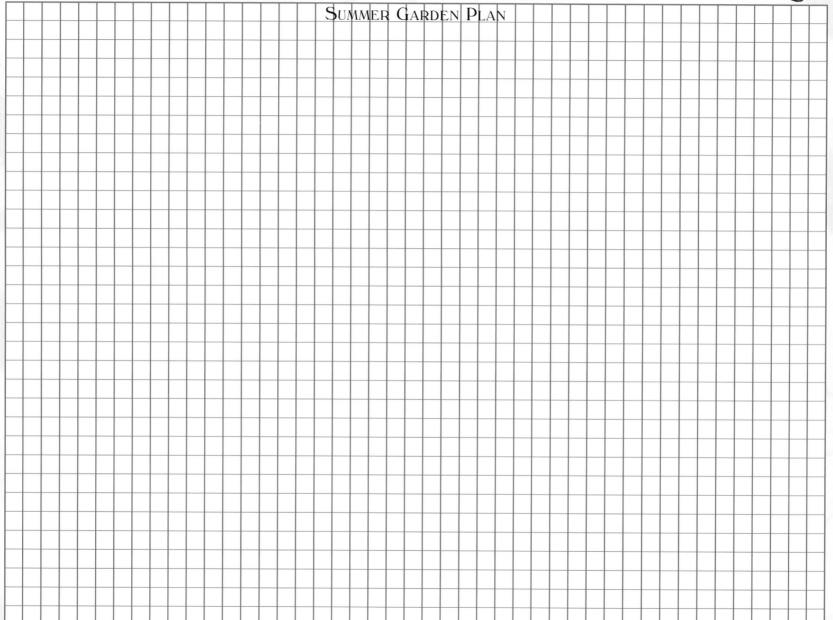

SPECIAL PROJECTS   FORWARD PLANNING IDEAS

SUMMER TASK LIST

AREA   WORK TO BE DONE

LAWNS/HEDGES

BEDDING PLANTS

ANNUALS

PERENNIALS

TREES/SHRUBS

ROSES

CLIMBERS

HERBS/VEGETABLES

FRUIT

CONTAINERS

PATHS/PATIOS

WATER GARDENS

MISCELLANEOUS

Key Tips for Early Summer

Draw the curtains in the house and shade the greenhouse to exclude all hot sunshine during your absence. This helps to protect all your plants during the time you are away.

This is the time to start thinking about next spring for a colourful display.
- *Forget-me-nots can be pulled up after flowering.*
- *Wallflowers, sweet william and Iceland poppies can be sown in pots or in the garden.*
- *Cover pansy seeds with seed compost and keep cool and dark. Check regularly – seedlings emerge in about two weeks. Plant outside or transfer to modules and grow on till mid autumn.*
Colourful winter pansies are popular and give pleasure right through until spring.

This is the time to ensure you work hard to train climbing roses. Try to get thorny branches where you want them and tie them well in. Sweet pea rings are useful for this and can be handled even with gloves on.

Warmer weather brings out garden pests to attack the contents of your vegetable garden at this time. Watch out for cabbage root fly and carrot fly. It is important to take precautions when you plant – a piece of old carpet will protect cabbages; carrots can be hidden amongst onions – the strong smell confuses the flies.

Watch out for fruit pests which disappear seconds after they have laid their eggs. There are various traps which will cut the problem drastically and protect your fruit crops.

Prepare for short supplies of water by installing a rainwater butt.

Plants for Early Summer

Campanula lactiflora
– traditional lavender for edging or ground cover combines well with roses.

Papaver nudicaule
Iceland poppy easily raised from seed produces a long season of blooms.

Bearded irises
– brightly coloured with a short season. Grow in mixed borders or in beds by themselves. Hardy plants in various categories.

'Comtesse de Bouchaud'
– versatile jackmanii clematis blooms profusely even on north facing wall.

Philadelphus coronarius
– a hardy mock orange shrub smothered with fragrant creamy blooms in early summer.

Digitalis purpurea
– white flowered foxglove.

RASPBERRIES
In the restricted space of a small garden raspberries can be grown as a pillar.
- *Tie the canes to wire; this will produce a smaller crop but it is both decorative and neat, taking up less room and easily covered with protective netting to deter birds and avoid frost.*

Plants in Flower at this Time

VIOLAS

Trim back any straggly violas.
*• Work in compost, water
occasionally and cut off the main
plant. Pot or plant in an empty
corner of the garden.*

PATIOS

*Paved areas and patios
can be brightened up
with the bright colours
of summer bedding
plants now. Later on
replace with bulbs and
small evergreen shrubs
continuing the colour
through autumn and
winter until the spring.*

POPPIES

*Once early flowering poppies are
finished, tidy them up ruthlessly,
cutting back to the base. Foliage
will re-grow and you may have
another late summer blooming.*

SUCCESSFUL PLANTS   UNSUCCESSFUL PLANTS

ANEMONIES
Plant as many anemones as you can in early summer – they are lovely towards the end of the season. Well watered, they will give a glorious display and you can store for replanting. For a continuous supply plant fresh tubers every year.

WEEDING
For stubborn weeds use a flame gun regularly throughout the summer.

Record of Purchases and Planting

NAME	TYPE OF PLANT	WHERE PURCHASED	WHERE PLANTED	DATE

NOTES, REMINDERS AND OBSERVATIONS

GREENHOUSES
When temperatures begin to rise tomatoes under glass need regular feeding and watering.

SUMMER PRUNING
After early flowering shrubs are finished they can be pruned. If it is warm you can do this in mid summer. Make sure you cut older branches down to a bottom sideshoot or right down to the base.

SUMMER HOLIDAYS
If you go away on holiday make sure you have arranged for regular watering – hanging baskets, containers and green house plants must be taken care of.
• Before you leave make sure you soak plants, weed the garden thoroughly and mow the lawn at the very last minute.

PREPARE FOR CHRISTMAS
If you want chicory in winter time, this is the time to sow in rich soil and a sunny position.

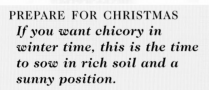

Mid Summer

KEY TASKS

LAWNS AND HEDGES
- *Control leylandii hedges; take cuttings.*
- *Continue to keep lawn in tip top condition.*

BEDDING PLANTS AND ANNUALS
- *Pick flowers and slowly dry them.*

PERENNIALS
- *Cut back perennials which have flowered to encourage second blooms.*
- *Take cuttings from carnations and pinks.*
- *Divide flag irises and plant.*

BULBS
- *Divide clumps of daffodils.*

HERBS AND VEGETABLES
- *Cut back herbs to encourage further growth.*
- *Sow plenty of autumn vegetables.*
- *Harvest shallots and garlic.*
- *Protect tomatoes from any disorders now.*

MISCELLANEOUS
- *In limited space of a small garden use a deep bed.*

Key Tips for Mid Summer

Irises are good flowers for a wide range of colours, which make a wonderful show in the garden each year. They are easy plants to grow and demand a well drained, dry sunny spot. Make sure you have dug in manure or compost before planting. Divide these plants every 3 or 4 years about five weeks after flowering ends.

Cut down early flowering herbaceous perennials now to avoid self seeding and future over-crowding.

Lift daffodils and split into individual bulbs. Dry off and store in a cool place to replant in autumn.

Soft tip cuttings of herbaceous perennials and shrubs can be taken now. They will root fast in high temperatures. Lavender especially benefits from replacement regularly every few years.

In a hot dry summer lawns will begin to suffer noticeably. Mow less frequently and leave the grass quite high. Allow cuttings to stay on the lawn for a thin mulch. Give an extra feed in autumn just before rain.

Plants for Mid Summer

Ipomoea purpurea – common morning glory
– half-hardy annual climber with large funnel shaped blooms.

Centaurea hypoleuca
- perennial cornflower with long lasting flowers which spread steadily.

Phlox paniculata
– herbaceous border phlox.

Lonicera x brownii 'Dropmore Scarlet'
– a hardy honeysuckle growing to 4m in sunny position. Long-lived with abundant trumpet shaped flowers. Blooms till late autumn.

BORDERS
In chalky soil, border carnations and garden pinks do exceptionally well.

DRYING FLOWERS
If you want to make an arrangement of dried flowers, many of them can be preserved if you pick them when they reach their best – just before they open fully.
• Hang upside down in a cool airy place to dry slowly in plenty of circulating air. Don't use the greenhouse or kitchen – they will shrivel up quickly.
• Preserve achillea, amaranthus, gypsophila, delphiniums, lavender, golden rod and zinnia.
True everlasting flowers include helipterum, helichrysum and rodanthe which are naturally long lasting with delicate papery petals.

PLANTS IN FLOWER AT THIS TIME

TOMATOES
Watch tomatoes for any disorders and take remedial action.

Place a picture of your garden in bloom at this time.

HERBS
Herbs respond well to a good cut and will produce new young leaves. Remember fertiliser and a good watering – this encourages fast regrowth.

62

SUCCESSFUL PLANTS

UNSUCCESSFUL PLANTS

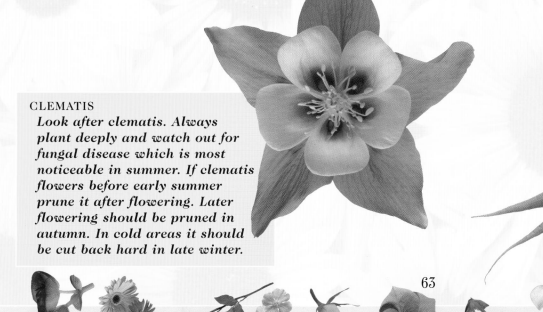

CLEMATIS
Look after clematis. Always plant deeply and watch out for fungal disease which is most noticeable in summer. If clematis flowers before early summer prune it after flowering. Later flowering should be pruned in autumn. In cold areas it should be cut back hard in late winter.

VEGETABLES
Keep harvesting the vegetable garden regularly. The more you pick, the more you will grow.

Record of Purchases and Planting

NAME	TYPE OF PLANT	WHERE PURCHASED	WHERE PLANTED	DATE

Notes, Reminders and Observations

CUTTINGS
Take conifer cuttings now if you want them.

SHALLOTS
Remember that shallots need to be ripened in hot sun to improve flavour and ensure bulbs keep for longer in store.

VEGETABLES
Plan autumn vegetables now, using any vacant ground.

GARLIC
Garlic needs sun to ripen well and can be dug up when leaves begin to turn colour.

PRUNING
Control fast growing leylandii now with a good clip. Repeat in early autumn.

Late Summer

KEY TASKS

LAWNS AND HEDGES
- *Trim hedges before growth begins to slow down.*
- *Prepare lawns for turfing or sowing.*
- *Seed new lawns.*

PERENNIALS
- *Watch out for self-set seedlings while weeding borders.*

TREES, SHRUBS AND CLIMBERS
- *Take cuttings from semi-ripe plants.*
- *Prune vigorous climbers and shrubs.*

BULBS
- *Plant autumn crocuses.*
- *Plant Madonna lilies for next year.*

HERBS AND VEGETABLES
- *Sow Chinese vegetables for autumn and winter picking.*
- *Protect late sown vegetables from both sun and frost.*

FRUIT
- *Cut down raspberry canes after use.*
- *Prune all trained fruit trees.*
- *Propagate from old strawberry plants and make new beds.*

CONTAINERS
- *Sow perennials for late blooming.*

MISCELLANEOUS
- *Take action to discourage slugs.*

66

KEY TIPS FOR LATE SUMMER

Plant autumn flowering bulbs in late summer. Think ahead and order them from a reputable mail order supplier early in the season.

Try to use up seeds from spring sowing to rejuvenate containers at this time. A late batch of flowers provides a welcome splash of colour.

Summer prune any vigorous climbers and shrubs now. Wisteria should be pruned in late summer – reduce side-shoots to 3-5 leaves. Rambling roses will also need attention at this time.

Now is the time to buy new strawberry plants. There are many varieties which can be grown in sequence to provide good crops throughout the season. Begin planning for next year.

This is a good time to turf a lawn or prepare to sow lawn seed. A well tended lawn enclosed by well packed borders provides a welcome oasis in any size garden.

PLANTS FOR LATE SUMMER

'Grandiflora'
– a hardy hydrangea which tolerates shade well and produces dramatic blooms.

'Madame Julia'
– a late flowering clematis with large foliage and flowers. A hardy plant which grows to 4m.

Bracteantha bracteata 'Drakar Mixed'
– bright coloured papery petalled straw flower.

Lavatera
– hardy shrub with large blooms similar to hollyhock; blooms throughout the summer.

Monarda didym
– a bee balm or bergamot in various colours of herbaceous flowering stems.

SOWING
This is the very last chance for sowing salads to harvest later in the year.

VEGETABLES
Chinese vegetables are used to mild winters and cool summers. They will grow through the autumn if sown after the longest day of the year.

67

PLANTS IN FLOWER AT THIS TIME

WEEDING
When weeding perennials look out for self seeded flowering plants.

ROSES
Remove faded flowers and regularly dead head roses.

SUCCESSFUL PLANTS   UNSUCCESSFUL PLANTS

PESTS
Slugs are a major garden threat. Use all means at your disposal to discourage them now.

Record of Purchases and Planting

NAME	TYPE OF PLANT	WHERE PURCHASED	WHERE PLANTED	DATE

NOTES, REMINDERS AND OBSERVATIONS

HEDGES

Remember to give hedges another good trim.

PRUNING

Summer prune fruit trees. When raspberries have fruited cut out old canes and tie in new ones.

THE GARDEN YEAR

AUTUMN

Season of mists and mellow fruitfulness

Close bosom-friend of the maturing sun;

Conspiring with him how to load and bless

With fruit the vine that round the thatch-eaves run

Keats

Early Autumn

KEY TASKS

LAWNS AND HEDGES
- *Take out weeds, giving lawns early autumn care.*

BEDDING PLANTS AND ANNUALS
- *Prepare dahlias, fuchsias and other perennials for over-wintering.*
- *Before the first frosts, take bedding plant cuttings.*

PERENNIALS
- *Collect ripe seeds and sow.*
- *Plant and divide hardy perennials.*
- *Overhaul borders.*

BULBS
- *Plant bulbs outside for spring and summer flowering.*

ROSES
- *Save seeds from rose hips and sow.*
- *Take cuttings.*

HERBS AND VEGETABLES
- *Sow and plant spring cabbage.*
- *Prepare to lift onions and plant new sets.*
- *Store squash to use during the winter.*

Place a picture here of

your garden in autumn

FRUIT
- *Pick and store fruit from trees.*

MISCELLANEOUS
- *Decide whether it is worthwhile buying a greenhouse before the winter.*

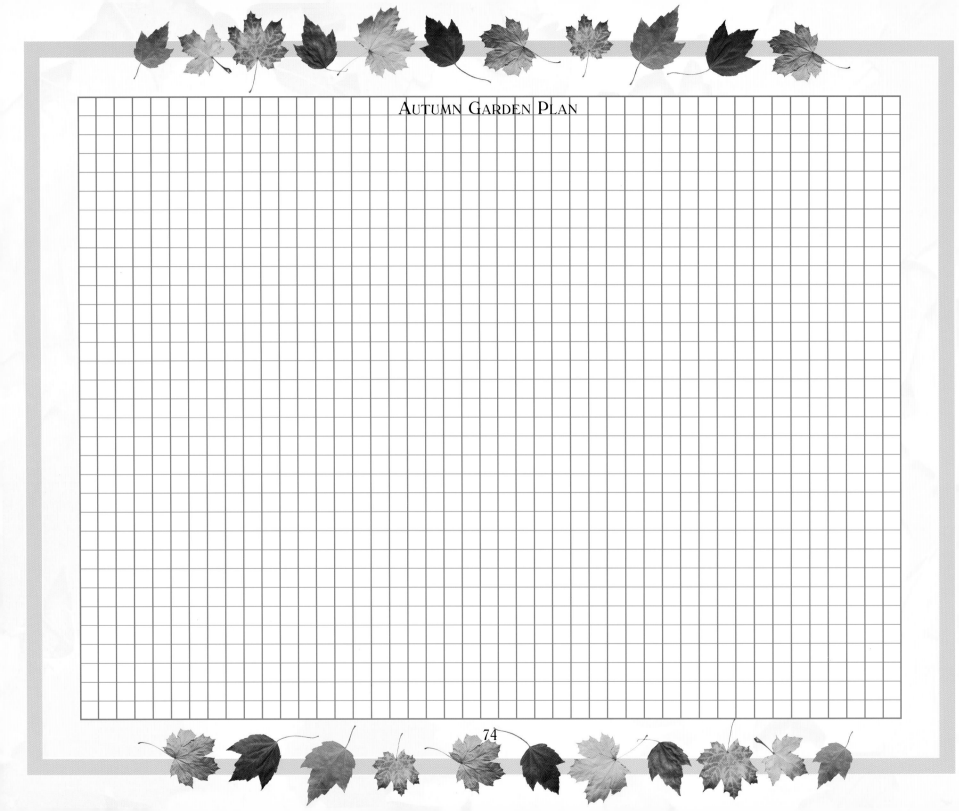

Autumn Garden Plan

SPECIAL PROJECTS

FORWARD PLANNING IDEAS

AUTUMN TASK LIST

AREA	WORK TO BE DONE
LAWNS/HEDGES	
BEDDING PLANTS	
ANNUALS	
PERENNIALS	
TREES/SHRUBS	
ROSES	
CLIMBERS	
HERBS/VEGETABLES	
FRUIT	
CONTAINERS	
PATHS/PATIOS	
WATER GARDENS	
MISCELLANEOUS	

KEY TIPS FOR EARLY AUTUMN

Leave dahlias outside until the first threat of frost.
- *Lift tubers and shake off soil.*
- *Trim off old stems.*
- *Put tubers upside down for a week to drain then pack in cardboard boxes – right way up, to store in cool place.*

Work manure or garden compost into soil to revive it after the summer.

Collect seeds from the garden – the cheapest way to produce lots of new plants for next year. Many hardy perennials can be sown as soon as they have been dried and will germinate quickly now or in the spring.

A wide range of bulbs available now will provide a bright garden next spring. Start with daffodils which could flower for a hundred days; the earliest variety start in late winter and end with those which finish flowering in late spring. Plant at the right depth.

Pumpkins, marrows and all winter squash vegetables must be well seasoned before storing. Cut when they are a good colour and have reached full size. Lie them in the sunshine for two weeks or so to harden. A greenhouse or sunny windowsill will protect them from the wet.

Remember the benefits of a greenhouse. It should repay its' initial cost in about two years. This is a good time to start thinking about buying one. Your choice of greenhouse will depend on your budget. You will get what you pay for and usually it is sensible to buy the best you can afford.

PLANTS FOR EARLY AUTUMN

Maple trees
– give rich autumn tints.

Sea holly
– is a herbaceous perennial which is colourful and hardy.

Rubra – Japanese blood grass
– a deciduous grass with bright red autumn tips is for good soils;

Viburnum opulus – dwarf guelder rose
– is a dense deciduous shrub with red berries and leaves in autumn.

BULBS
Buy specially prepared hyacinth bulbs for forcing indoors to flower during winter.

BULBS
Crocuses can go into the ground now. Plant mixed colours in groups in the sun and cover with 5cm of soil.

77

PLANTS IN FLOWER AT THIS TIME

BORDERS
*Overhaul borders now starting
with herbaceous perennials.
Plant new perennials. Water
them in well.*

VEGETABLES
*Plant spring cabbages sown in late
summer in seedbeds. Take care that flea
beetles do not destroy them. The leaves
can be treated to avoid these pests.*

ROSES
*Rose cuttings can be
taken any time from now
until mid winter. You
will need strong healthy
stems – cut from low
down on the bush.*

BULBS
*New daffodils can be started
off in pots plunged in compost
outside until the spring.*

SUCCESSFUL PLANTS

UNSUCCESSFUL PLANTS

ROSES
Propagate some of your favourite roses now from seeds or cuttings.

LAWNS
Lawn care continues. If the summer has been dry, intensive care is needed now. Remove weeds with deep roots rake out dead growth.

FRUIT
Early apples, which do not store well, may be picked and eaten now.

VEGETABLES
Courgettes will store well until mid winter and keep like marrows.

ONIONS
Prepare to lift main crop onions now and plant autumn onion sets.

Record of Purchases and Planting

NAME	TYPE OF PLANT	WHERE PURCHASED	WHERE PLANTED	DATE

NOTES, REMINDERS AND OBSERVATIONS

FRUIT
Pick and store pears carefully to ensure perfect fruit for eating.

BULBS
Remember that you can also plant summer flowering bulbs now.

FRUIT
Hungry birds may peck your ripening fruit and begin rotting take steps to deter them now.

FUCHSIAS
Bring fuchsias in to pot them and keep in a heated greenhouse or cool well lit room to continue growing.

Mid Autumn

KEY TASKS

LAWNS AND HEDGES
• *Choose conifer or deciduous hedges.*
• *Plan spaces where hedges are to grow.*
• *Plant all kinds of hedges.*

TREES, SHRUBS AND CLIMBERS
• *Move large shrubs*
• *While soil is still warm, take hardwood cuttings.*
• *Now is the time to plant new shrubs and trees.*

HERBS AND VEGETABLES
• *Protect all late vegetables against frosts.*
• *Before the weather begins to turn too cold, plant garlic.*
• *Lift and store all root crops.*

FRUIT
• *Pick all apples.*
• *Prune blackcurrants.*
• *Protect apple and pear trees from winter moth.*
• *Buy a fruit cage and protect crops next year.*

CONTAINERS
• *Plant autumn and winter outdoor containers.*

MISCELLANEOUS
• *Start gentle digging.*

KEY TIPS FOR MID AUTUMN

For winter containers choose wood, clay or stone for extra protection from frost.
• Before frosts arrive wrap your pots with sacking or bubble polythene to avoid your plants freezing.

Plant pots for winter. Begin by ensuring good drainage and use good compost on top. Bulbs will give early colour; evergreens in the centre provide height. Choose good bushy plants and remember that winter pansies, wallflowers and forget-me-nots will give extra variety.

You could plant a boundary hedge now to ensure privacy from neighbours in the future. In a windy spot a hedge makes an excellent windbreak. In small gardens take care that your hedge does not take up too much precious space. Look at both deciduous and coniferous hedges and perhaps mix them.

Lift and store root crops now. A few vegetables can be left in the ground – celeriac, parsnips and salsify gain flavour after a touch of frost.

Garlic which has been exposed to two or three months of cold weather early on is best planted now. Try to buy seed bulbs and prepare a sunny spot to develop fat bulbs for next summer.

FRUIT TREES
If your garden is small, plan carefully for the right trees to give you colour and fruit. A good supplier will advise you on your choice.

PLANTS FOR MID AUTUMN

Boston ivy
– a hardy deciduous climber will even grow on north facing walls.

Brugmansia
– these vigorous semi-evergreen shrubs are best grown in containers and should be brought indoors now.

Cyclamen
– blooms appear during the autumn months.

'Honorine Jobert'
– a Japanese anemone is a late flowering perennial.

'Fructo Luteo'
– a deciduous tree. One of a variety of rowans, it grows to 6m.

SHRUBS AND TREES
This is the best time for planting deciduous shrubs and trees.

PLANTS IN FLOWER AT THIS TIME

CLIMBERS
Clematis can be planted and leaned against a support wall or trellis until it is established.

EVERGREENS
Evergreens will continue to lose a certain amount of water throughout the winter but will also benefit from planting now.

SUCCESSFUL PLANTS

UNSUCCESSFUL PLANTS

FRUIT
*Prune blackcurrants
when the leaves
have turned colour.*

FRUIT
*Most main crop apples
will be ready to pick now.
If they are sound and ripe
they will keep well for a
couple of months if stored.*

VEGETABLES
*Put cloches over the last of
your summer vegetables.*

Record of Purchases and Planting

NAME	TYPE OF PLANT	WHERE PURCHASED	WHERE PLANTED	DATE

NOTES, REMINDERS AND OBSERVATIONS

WORMS

Earthworms need encouragement to work hard in your garden – provide them with plenty of organic material.

DIGGING

This is the perfect time of the year for digging. The weather is cool and the soil will be moist.

Late Autumn

KEY TASKS

LAWNS AND HEDGES
• *Prepare soil and lay turf.*

ROSES
• *After leaves have fallen, plant roses.*

BULBS
• *Between now and mid spring, plant lilies.*
• *During late autumn, plant tulips.*

HERBS AND VEGETABLES
• *Before the ground freezes lift winter leeks.*

FRUIT
• *Winter prune now.*
• *Plant new apple and pear trees now.*

MISCELLANEOUS
• *Greenhouses should be insulated for the winter.*
• *Sweep up all autumn leaves and stack them to make leaf mould.*
• *All alpines should be protected from rain.*
• *Plants must be protected from frost.*

Key Tips for Late Autumn

Prepare to plant late flowering tulips in the first half of winter after all other spring bulbs.
• *They need a light soil and a sunny spot; try to avoid mixed borders.*

Bare-rooted roses can be bought now and will be better than container grown plants. The best time for planting is when they have lost their leaves.

It is more expensive to lay a lawn with turf than to grow from seed. If you prefer the instant finish, make sure you buy the best turves you can which are guaranteed weed free. This is the best time of the year to lay turf but delay if the ground is very wet or frozen. Only water if the weather is exceptionally dry.

The dark strong leaves of winter leeks improve their flavour after frost.
• *They can be lifted and stored in compost in a shed to last through several months.*

Plant new apple and pear trees now. Carefully assess the amount of space available in your garden before making your final choice. There are several varieties of frost tolerant apples and pears which will be happy in colder regions.

Your greenhouse will retain more warmth if it is insulated. Bubble polythene can be fixed inside the glass. Keep the greenhouse well ventilated on mild days – a small crack of air for about an hour will help keep disease at bay. Protect container plants carefully.

Plants for Late Autumn

Clematis orientalis 'Bill Mackensie'
– produces silver seedheads lasting through the winter months.

Lonicera fragrantissima
– continues to produce fragrant flowers.

Chrysanthemums
– flower in perennial borders well into winter if they are in a sheltered sunny spot.

Vitis coignetiae
– provides a display of crimson leaves through the autumn . A hardy self clinging climbing vine.

LILIES
Between now and mid spring is the best time to plant lilies outside.

PLANTS IN FLOWER AT THIS TIME

_____
_____
_____
_____
_____
_____
_____
_____
_____
_____
_____

FROST
*Protect plants against frost.
How you do this depends on
the type of plant.*

_____
_____
_____
_____

*Place a picture of your
garden in bloom at this time.*

SUCCESSFUL PLANTS

UNSUCCESSFUL PLANTS

ALPINES
Alpines need some help in a relatively mild climate.
• *Provide them with good drainage and mulch them well.*
• *Cover with plastic or glass to keep them dry.*

CHICORY
Chicory seeds sown in early summer should have roots which are now ready to dig up and force.

91

RECORD OF PURCHASES AND PLANTING

NAME	TYPE OF PLANT	WHERE PURCHASED	WHERE PLANTED	DATE

NOTES, REMINDERS AND OBSERVATIONS

COMPOST
Leafmould contains lots of goodness for potting composts and vegetable plots. Make your own by raking up fallen leaves to rot down and store in a wire netting enclosure.

PRUNING
Tackle winter pruning of fruit bushes and trees now.

THE GARDEN YEAR

WINTER

See, winter comes to rule the varied year,

Sullen and sad.

James Thomson

Early Winter

KEY TASKS

BEDDING PLANTS AND ANNUALS
- *Buy pelargonium plugs to flower in the summer or sow seeds now.*

TREES, SHRUBS AND CLIMBERS
- *To prevent winter damage to long stems, tie in or shorten them.*
- *Give deciduous trees shape by pruning.*

BULBS
- *Begin to pot batches of lilies.*

HERBS AND VEGETABLES
- *For small gardens, choose mini-vegetables.*

FRUIT
- *Plant blackberries and prune existing plants.*

MISCELLANEOUS
- *Plan winter border colour schemes.*
- *Prepare a hot bed to force early crops for the spring.*

Place a picture here of

your garden in winter

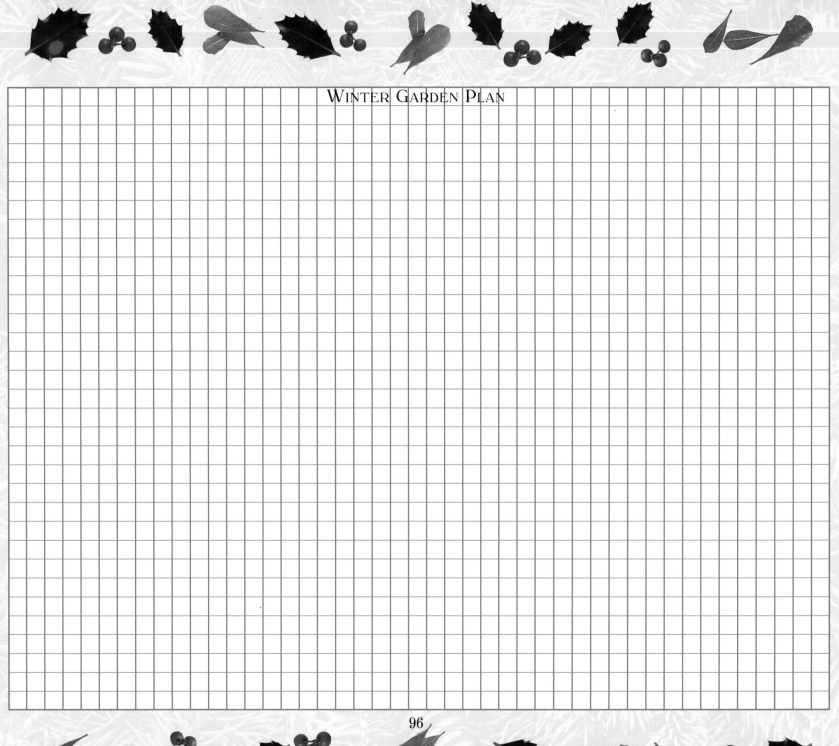

Winter Garden Plan

SPECIAL PROJECTS

FORWARD PLANNING IDEAS

Winter Task List

AREA   WORK TO BE DONE

LAWNS/HEDGES

BEDDING PLANTS

ANNUALS

PERENNIALS

TREES/SHRUBS

ROSES

CLIMBERS

HERBS/VEGETABLES

FRUIT

CONTAINERS

PATHS/PATIOS

WATER GARDENS

MISCELLANEOUS

Key Tips for Early Winter

You can grow pelargoniums from seed and this is the right time.
• Use a propagator because the seeds need a temperature of at least 65°F to germinate.

When the leaves of deciduous trees have fallen they can be pruned and shaped. Small gardens may benefit from reducing the overall size and branches can be thinned.
• Hard pruning promotes new growth.

Prevent wind damage to long stemmed roses, shrubs and climbers this month by cutting back or tying in.

On the days when the sun does shine go and check the vegetable garden.

After a hard frost make sure that any new plants have not lifted. If necessary firm them down.

Plants for Early Winter

Asian mahonia x media 'Charity'
– a hardy ever-green shrub with long leaves and delicately scented blooms.

'Gilt Edge'
– bushy evergreen oleaster, variegated leaves.

Jasminium nudiflorum
– winter flowering jasmine produces bright yellow flowers till early spring.

Cotoneaster x waterei
– semi-evergreen bush with clusters of brightly coloured winter berries.

LILIES
Lilies can be planted in pots in early winter for planting out in the spring.

99

PLANTS IN FLOWER AT THIS TIME

Place a picture of your

garden in bloom at this time.

BORDERS
During the winter plan
border colour schemes.

SUCCESSFUL PLANTS   UNSUCCESSFUL PLANTS

Record of Purchases and Planting

NAME	TYPE OF PLANT	WHERE PURCHASED	WHERE PLANTED	DATE

NOTES, REMINDERS AND OBSERVATIONS

FRUIT
It is the right time of year to plant new blackberry canes; remember to prune the old ones.

103

Mid Winter

Key Tasks

LAWNS AND HEDGES
- *Spike the lawn to improve drainage.*

BEDDING PLANTS AND ANNUALS
- *Buy new sowing compost.*
- *Save time and space – sow in modules.*
- *Sow sweet peas.*

PERENNIALS
- *Take root cuttings from border perennials.*

TREES, SHRUBS AND CLIMBERS
- *Prune trees and shrubs grown for leaf colour.*
- *Shape young trees.*
- *Check supports of older trees and stake new ones.*

HERBS AND VEGETABLES
- *Set up early potatoes to sprout.*
- *Plan for an early start to grow the years' vegetables.*

FRUIT
- *Prune hazelnut trees.*
- *Bring strawberry plants in to force in pots.*

CONTAINERS
- *Alpines in gritty compost, in clay pots can be plunged in sand/gravel beds in an unheated greenhouse.*

PATHS AND PATIOS
- *Continue weeding where necessary.*

Key Tips for Mid Winter

Order deep frozen runners from specialist suppliers for spring delivery. When planted the sudden change in temperature means that they can crop in only 60 days after planting.

Young plants and cuttings in the greenhouse benefit from the gentle warmth of a heated mat trapped under a polythene cover. Heating a whole greenhouse at this time of year is too expensive many plants can be raised indoors on windowsills or in the airing cupboard.

Lawns which squelch underfoot need spiking to remedy poor drainage.
• *Use a hollow-tine aerator or garden fork to spike lawns – push in 15cm deep.*

Start to think about vegetables to harvest later in the season; make first sowings indoors. Prepare soil for later planting.
• *Cover area set aside for first plantings with thick polythene sheeting or cloches to keep bed dry and warm.*
• *On windowsills or in the greenhouse start sowing seeds for plants to be ready to go outside from late winter.*

Sow small quantities – early cabbage, cauliflower and lettuce which do not need high temperatures and germinate at 55°F.
• *When big enough prick them out to 5cm and grow on in light.*

Start early potatoes; order seed potatoes now in time for preparation before planting out in spring. Sprout or chit to advance first harvest and increase crop size.

Plants for Mid Winter

Corylus avellana
– Corkscrew hazel for golden catkins in early spring.

Skimmias
– slow growing robust shrubs – fragrant blooms and evergreen leaves.

Pallida – soft coloured witch hazel
– for sweet fragrance.

Pernettya
– shade tolerant evergreen with heavy crops of berries.

Hedera helix – English ivy
– hardy self clinging evergreen grows to 16ft.

SOWING
Sow sweet peas now.
• *Raise plants in plastic modules 4cm across.*
• *Use modules for tender annuals and perennials.*

Plants in Flower at this Time

SOWING IN SEED TRAYS
• *Sow on top of compost thinly.*
• *To provide darkness for germination sieve thin layer of compost on top.*
• *Cover tray with glass or clear plastic to keep seeds moist.*
• *Add newspaper if required – remove when first seedlings show.*

Primed seeds have been started into growth and dried before packaging. Some seeds need light to germinate – check the seed packet before sowing to avoid failure.

Propagate plants by root cuttings. Those taken from variegated plants lose their varied colour – leaves will be green.

TO TAKE ROOT CUTTINGS
• *Dig up plant and wash soil off roots to make separation easier.*
• *Cut off sound roots to pencil thickness; divide into sections 5cm long; trim fibrous roots.*
• *Cut top straight and bottom diagonally.*
• *Place upright in pot of cutting compost.*
• *Just bury tops and water well.*
• *Stand in cold frame to protect from frost.*
• *Faster rooting needs heated propagator.*

STRAWBERRIES
Buy pot grown strawberries for cropping later in the season.

ALPINES
Sow alpines from seed – saxifrages, pinks, tiny primulas, stonecrops and houseleeks.
• *Leave seeds outside to freeze naturally – the cold triggers germination when temperature rises.*

SOWING
Pinks, delphiniums, nasturtiums and marigolds grow well in modules.

SUCCESSFUL PLANTS

UNSUCCESSFUL PLANTS

SOWING
start garlic cloves and sow ferns.

SOWING
Early vegetables can be grown in clusters – leeks and carrots 6-8 seeds in a cell.

STRAWBERRIES
Strawberries which were potted up last summer can come into the greenhouse for early blossoming and fruiting in late spring.
• Push outdoor crops ahead and cover with double thickness of fleece or cloches.
• Take off any damaged leaves and use organic fertiliser. Keep out draughts.

ALPINES
Alpines are tough and adapt to harsh environments. If grown in gritty soil, which is well drained in a raised bed, they will survive the worst winter.

107

Record of Purchases and Planting

NAME	TYPE OF PLANT	WHERE PURCHASED	WHERE PLANTED	DATE

TREES
Ornamental trees need to have feathers removed gradually starting with the bottom and working up year by year.

FRUIT TREES
Young fruit trees may have sideshoots on the trunks which can be turned into fruiting spurs.

WEEDING
Chickweed and groundsel need continuous weeding to avoid a spring invasion.

109

Late Winter

KEY TASKS

BEDDING PLANTS AND ANNUALS
• *Revive stored dahlias for cuttings.*
• *Watch young seedlings under glass.*

PERENNIALS
• *Take basal cuttings from any strong young shoots.*

TREES, SHRUBS AND CLIMBERS
• *Re-shape conifers after any snow and frost damage.*
• *Prune any late flowering clematis.*
• *Prune any late flowering shrubs.*

BULBS
• *For early colour, indoors and out, force spring bulbs.*
• *Start achimenes, begonias and gloxinias.*

ROSES
• *During the latter part of winter, start pruning.*

HERBS AND VEGETABLES
• *Plan tender greenhouse crops and tomatoes.*
• *Sow vegetables for early crops under cloches.*
• *This is the time to plant shallots.*

FRUIT
• *Choose currants, gooseberries and raspberries and plant.*
• *Force early picking rhubarb.*

MISCELLANEOUS
• *Buy or make cloches to protect early sowing.*
• *Plan ahead to use cloches effectively.*

110

KEY TIPS FOR LATE WINTER

Look after seedlings. Keep an eye on your seedlings as they begin to come up – they need plenty of light. If they are indoors make sure they are on the windowsill.

Make a light box for seedlings.
- *Cut the front out of a large cardboard box.*
- *Paint the inside white – this forms a reflector.*
- *line the base with foil and use this to ensure your seedlings get plenty of light without being scorched by sun or killed by cold.*

Put your light box on a table by the sunniest window – be prepared to give your seedlings the protection of a sheet of newspaper when necessary.

Bring out your stored dahlias and other perennials now. The boxes of compost in which they have spent the winter should be topped up and they need a little water. Spray them occasionally – it helps to stimulate the growth of the strongest shoots.

Bring any potted spring bulbs indoors to force them. Put them on a sunny windowsill in a cool room till flower buds colour – then bring them into a warmer room to enjoy them.

If heavy snow has misplaced branches of conifers tie them back to the main branch with plastic coated wire protected by thick sacking to prevent wire from cutting the stems.

Now is the time to begin planning sowing of tomatoes in the greenhouse. Choose a variety well known for flavour. Sow seeds in gentle heat and transplant to pots when a full pair of seed leaves appear. In mid spring they will be ready to plant out in the greenhouse.

PLANTS FOR LATE WINTER/EARLY SPRING

'Silver Queen'
– bright variegated evergreen. Small, compact shrub, climbs to 1.8m against a wall.

'Dawn' viburnum
– small fragrant blooms cluster on bare stems during the winter months.

Winter flowering heather 'Arthur Johnson'
– A spreading evergreen shrub with long sprays of flowers.

Lenten rose 'helleboris orientalis'
– evergreen perennial in various colours.

'Debbie' – camellia x williams ii
– evergreen shrub withstands exposure and cold. Large flowers.

ORNAMENTAL TREES
Ornamental conifers provide important solid features in the garden during the winter. A covering of snow or frost adds to their decorative appeal.

TUBERS
Start off begonias, gloxinias and achimenes in a conservatory or greenhouse now. Keep warm and evenly moist. Half bury tubers in trays of compost.

Plants in Flower at this Time

BASAL CUTTINGS

Some plants you can propagate from basal cuttings: Achillea, chrysanthemums, campanula, gypsophila, macleaya, marjoram, pyrethrum and thalictrum.
- *Scrape away some soil to expose base of young shoots 5-8cm long.*
- *Cut off with sharp knife near to crown.*
- *Trim cuttings remove older leaves and ragged edges.*
- *Dip ends in hormone rooting powder.*
- *Plant in moist compost and water in.*
- *Cover with plastic bag to retain humidity.*
- *Stand in gentle heat of propagator or cold frame.*
- *Wait for new fresh growth to show cuttings have rooted.*

BULBS

Crocus and snowdrops look perfect in a sunny spot in your garden this month.

ROSES

You can safely prune roses in late winter. Pruning of all roses:
- *Remove dead and damaged wood, stems and weak shoots.*
- *Continue pruning bushy roses – shorten strong stems to half their length.*
- *Cut should slope just above a bud.*

PRUNING

Cut back any clematis flowering after early summer to a few inches from the ground. For higher flowering cut back nearly to base of last year's growth.

PRUNING

It is best to prune late flowering shrubs now. Continue whenever weather permits up till mid spring.

SUCCESSFUL PLANTS

UNSUCCESSFUL PLANTS

VEGETABLES
Soil covered last month should now be dry enough to sow broad beans, cabbage, carrots, cauliflowers, lettuce, salad onions, spinach and turnips.

VEGETABLES
Aubergines can be started now – they need a longer growing season.

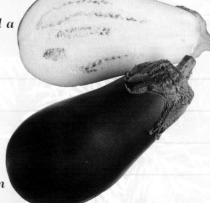

RHUBARB
This is the month to start forced rhubarb for superb flavour.

VEGETABLES
Under cloches early vegetables are safe from rain, wind and insects.

Record of Purchases and Planting

NAME	TYPE OF PLANT	WHERE PURCHASED	WHERE PLANTED	DATE

Notes, Reminders and Observations

SHALLOTS
Late winter is perfect for planting many varieties of shallots.

FRUIT
Choose soft fruit plants that you like now and get them started. All bush fruits need well manured soil, sun and shelter from frost.

PERSONAL GARDEN RECORDS

Oh, Adam was a gardener, and God who made him sees

That half a proper gardener's work is done upon his knees,

So when your work is finished, you can wash your hands and pray

For the glory of the garden, that it may not pass away.

Kipling

Annual Shows Visited

DATE   PLACE   COMMENTS

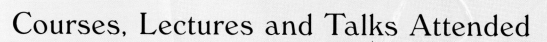

Courses, Lectures and Talks Attended

DATE	PLACE	SPEAKER	POINTS TO REMEMBER

Gardens Visited

DATE	PLACE/NAME OF GARDEN	COMMENTS

Contact Names and Addresses

NAME

ADDRESS

CONTACT NAME

TELEPHONE

COMMENTS

NAME

ADDRESS

CONTACT NAME

TELEPHONE

COMMENTS

NAME

ADDRESS

CONTACT NAME

TELEPHONE

COMMENTS

NAME

ADDRESS

CONTACT NAME

TELEPHONE

COMMENTS

120

NAME

ADDRESS

CONTACT NAME

TELEPHONE

COMMENTS

NAME

ADDRESS

CONTACT NAME

TELEPHONE

COMMENTS

NAME

ADDRESS

CONTACT NAME

TELEPHONE

COMMENTS

NAME

ADDRESS

CONTACT NAME

TELEPHONE

COMMENTS

NAME

ADDRESS

CONTACT NAME

TELEPHONE

COMMENTS

NAME

ADDRESS

CONTACT NAME

TELEPHONE

COMMENTS

NAME

ADDRESS

CONTACT NAME

TELEPHONE

COMMENTS

NAME

ADDRESS

CONTACT NAME

TELEPHONE

COMMENTS

NAME

ADDRESS

CONTACT NAME

TELEPHONE

COMMENTS

NAME

ADDRESS

CONTACT NAME

TELEPHONE

COMMENTS

NAME

ADDRESS

CONTACT NAME

TELEPHONE

COMMENTS

NAME

ADDRESS

CONTACT NAME

TELEPHONE

COMMENTS

Spring Reminders

Tasks	Date completed					
	Year 1	Year 2	Year 3	Year 4	Year 5	Year 6
Pruning						
Weeding						
Spraying						
Mulching						
Sowing						
Planting						
Dead heading						
Lawns						
Top-dressing						
General repairs						
preparation						

Summer Reminders

Tasks	Date completed					
	YEAR 1	YEAR 2	YEAR 3	YEAR 4	YEAR 5	YEAR 6
Lawns						
Cutting back						
Pruning						
Staking						
Weeding						
Spraying						
Watering						

Autumn Reminders

Tasks	Date completed					
	year 1	year 2	year 3	year 4	year 5	year 6
Weeding						
Pruning						
Transplanting						
Mulching						
Lawns						
Leaves						
Division						
Cuttings						
Planting						
Winter protection						

Winter Reminders

TASKS	DATE COMPLETED					
	YEAR 1	YEAR 2	YEAR 3	YEAR 4	YEAR 5	YEAR 6
WINTER PROTECTION						
PRUNING						
WATERING						
TRANSPLANTING						
GENERAL REPAIRS						
SERVICING						
ORDERS						

Buy my English posies!

Kent and Surrey may –

Violets of the Undercliff

Wet with Channel spray;

Cowslips from a Devon combe -

Midland furze afire –

Buy my English posies,

And I'll sell your hearts' desire!

Kipling